# planet earth

our extraordinary world

# Awesome Animals!

Modern Publishing
A Division of Unisystems, Inc.
New York, New York 10022
Printed in the the U.S.A
Series UPC: 49060

# Lions

# Jaguar

**Coyotes are spread across Alaska, Canada, USA, Mexico and Central America.**

# Waterfall

1.

2.

3.

4.

# FUNNY FROGS

One of these frogs is different from the others.
Circle him!

See Answers

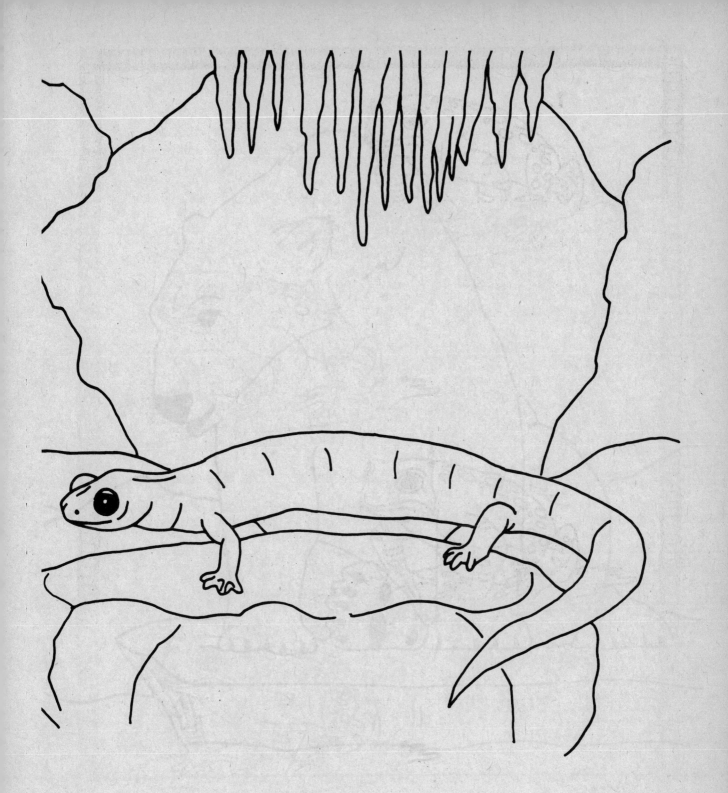

**The cave salamander is able to survive for up to 6 years without food.**

**Polar Bear**

# Elephants' ears are so big to help keep them cool.

# Aardvark

# Llama

**2.**

# ZEBRA FUN

These zebras are missing their stripes! Draw some stripes on them and be creative!

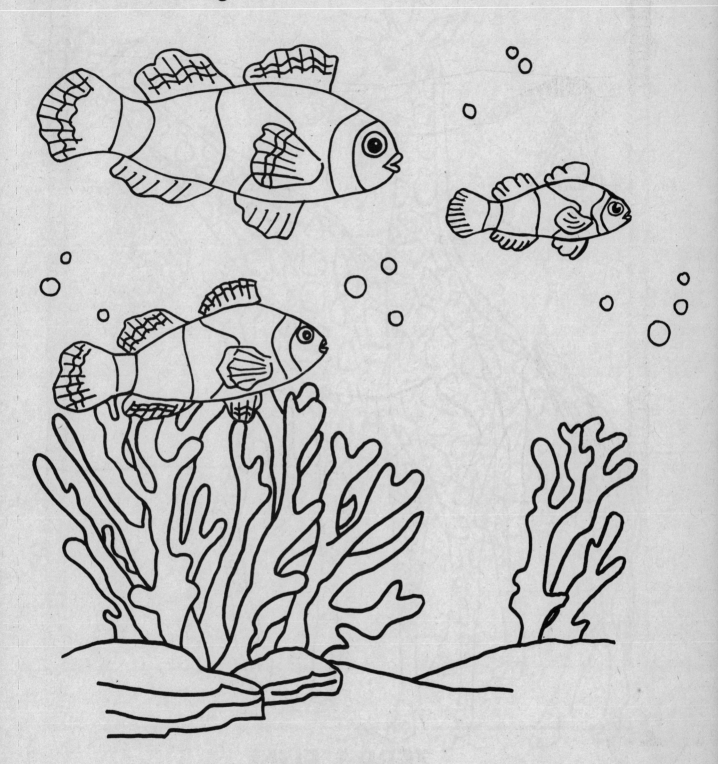

# Clownfish

# Giraffes

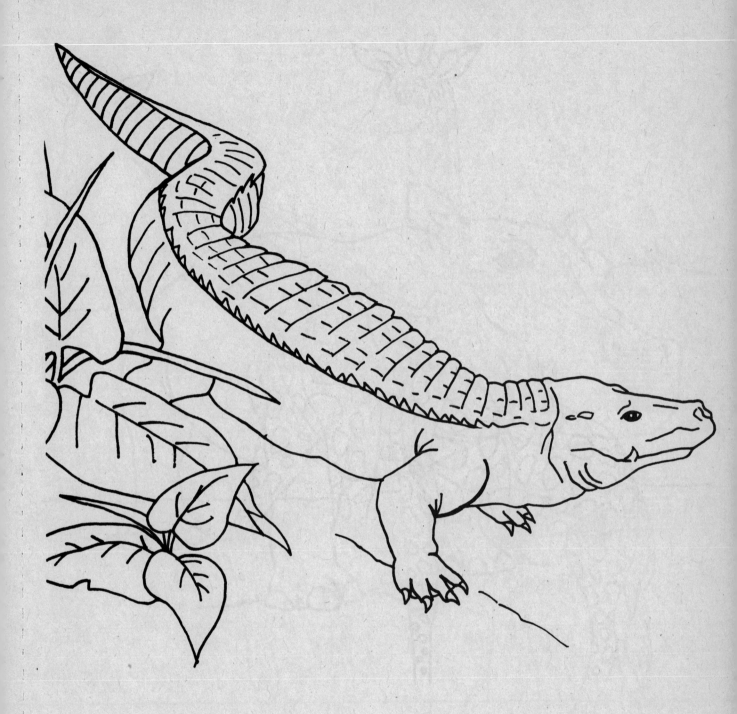

# Alligator

# Hippopotamus

# Bear Cubs

1.

2.

3.

4.

# OCEAN WONDERS

Which animal would you not find in the ocean? Circle it!

See Answers

**No two striped coats on zebras are the same – just like our fingerprints!**

**Parrot**

# Gazelle

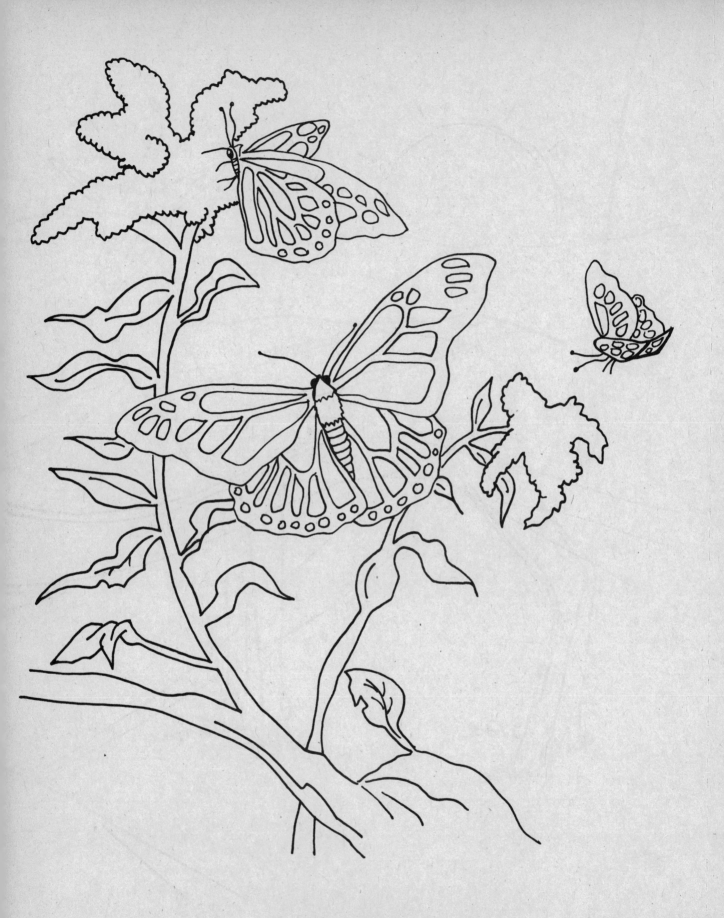

# Butterflies

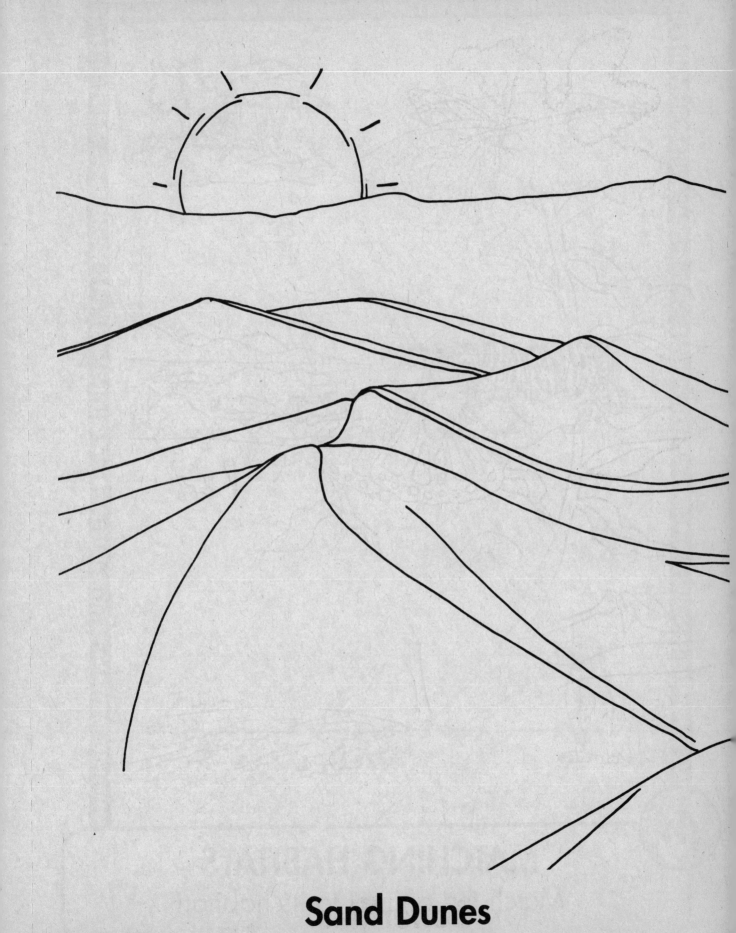

# Sand Dunes

**4.**

# MATCHING HABITATS
Match the animal to its habitat!

See Answers

# Chimpanzee

# Frog

# Penguins

**Parrots are vocal birds; they make "screaming" calls to communicate to each other.**

# A giant panda eats up to 88 pounds of bamboo a day.

1.

2.

3.

4.

# 5

# SIMILAR SNAKES

Which two snakes are identical? Circle your answer!

See Answers

**There are 2 species of hippo, both found in Africa.**

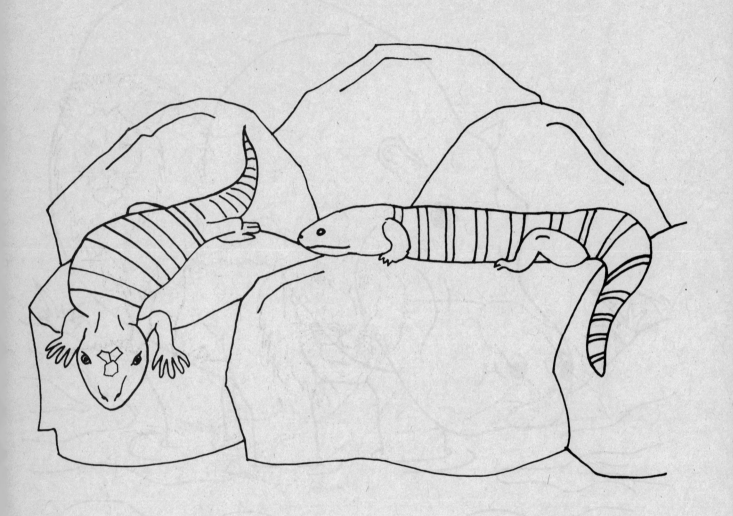

# Common Lizards

# Lions

# Giraffes

# Moose

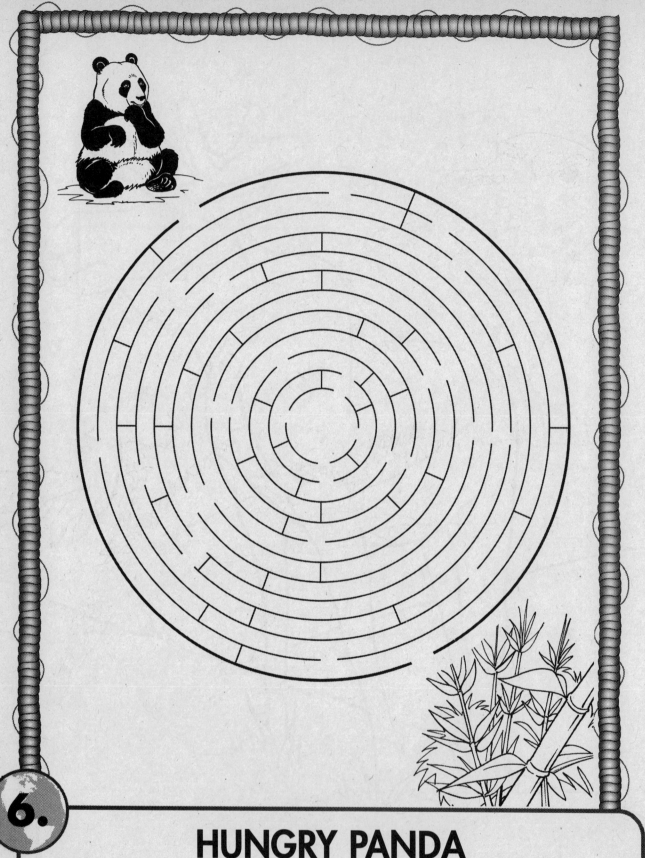

# 6

# HUNGRY PANDA

Help the hungry panda bear to his bamboo
by following the path through the maze!

See Answers

# Lizard

# Wolves

**Forests cover 1/3 of the Earth's surface.**

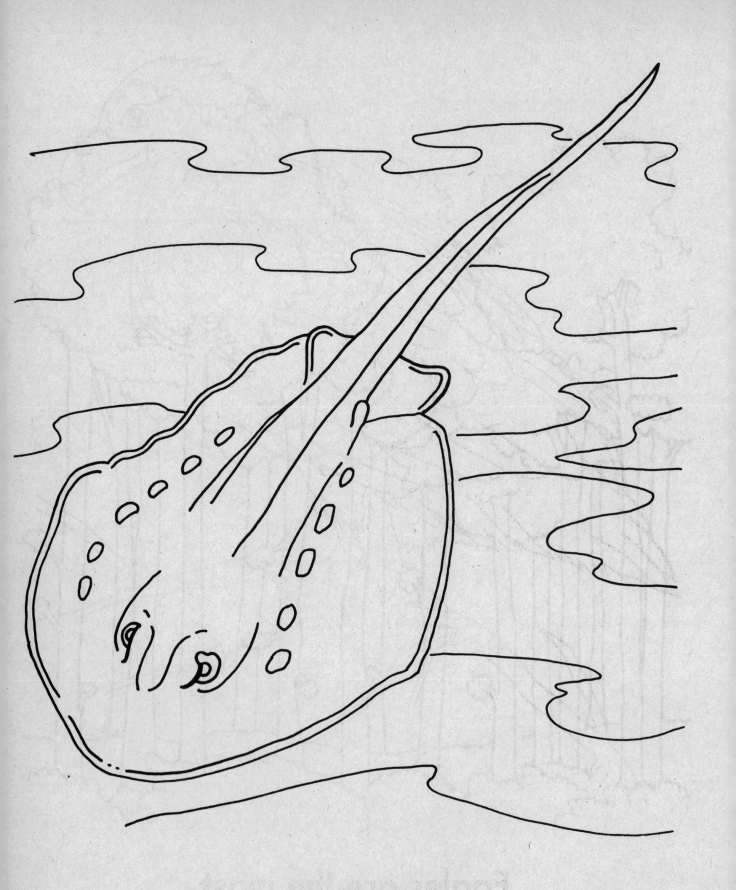

**Stingray**

**Eagles are the most magnificent birds of prey.**

# Gorilla

_____

_____

_____

**7.**

# BEARY FUN

Can you name 3 different types of bears in less than 1 minute? Go!

See Answers

# Geese

**Seal**

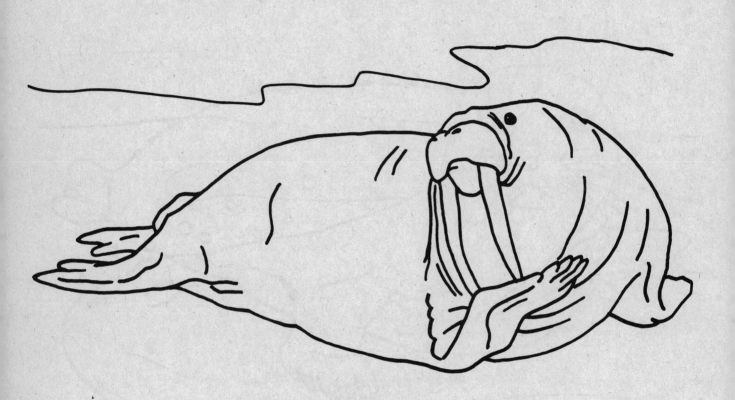

**Walrus**

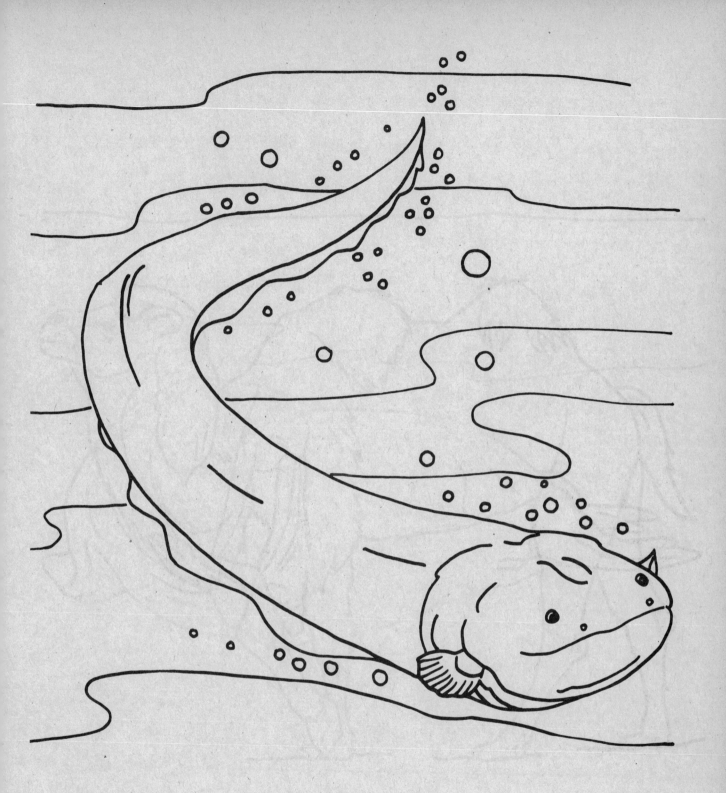

**Electric Eel**

# Camel

# Sea Gulls

_____

_____

_____

**8.**

# ANIMAL SLOWPOKES

Can you name 3 animals that move very slowly? Write your answers on the lines!

See Answers

**Cactus**

# Lion

# Antelopes

# Arctic Foxes

**Tortoises**

# Crabs

# TIGER TIME

How many tigers do you see on this page?
Write your answer on the line!

See Answers

# Mountain Goats

# Grizzly Bear

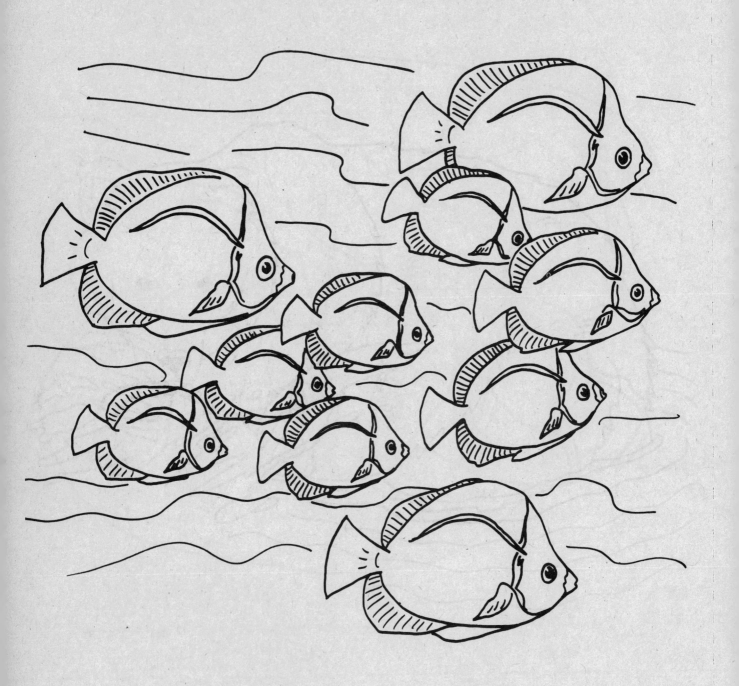

# Fish

**Anaconda**

**Crocodile**

# The toucan's most
# prominent feature is its bill.

# E A G L E

_____     _____

_____     _____

_____     _____

_____     _____

**10.**

## ENDANGERED SPECIES WORD PLAY

How many three- and four-letter words can you make from the letters in the words ENDANGERED SPECIES. Write them on the lines.

See Answers

**Woodpeckers are not
often seen on the ground.**

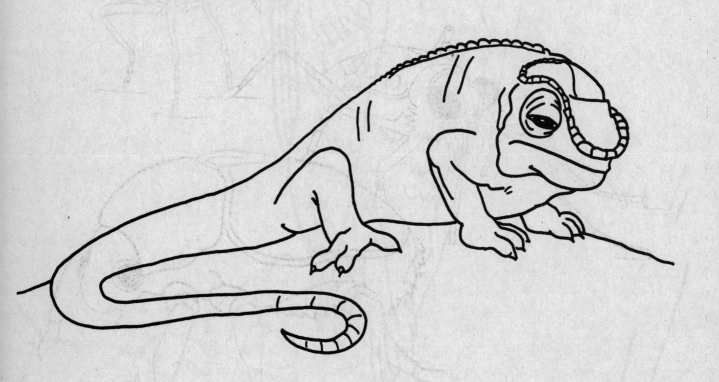

**Chameleons change their skin color to adapt to their environment**

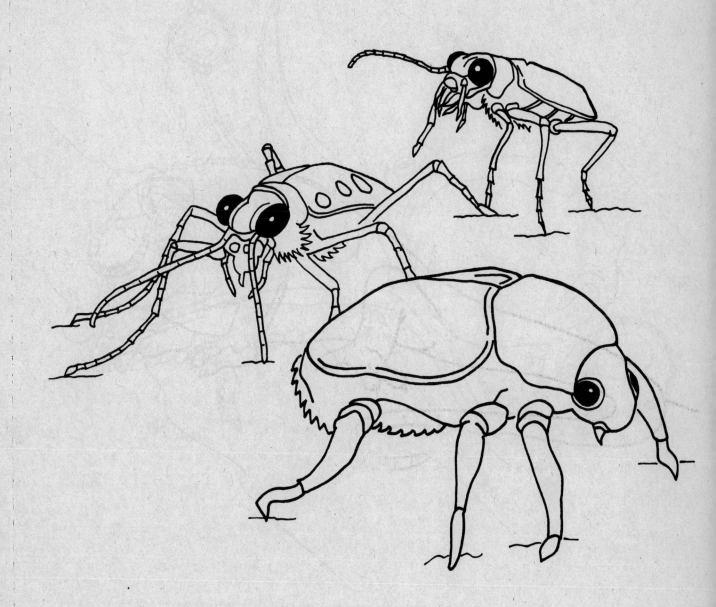

**Beetles**

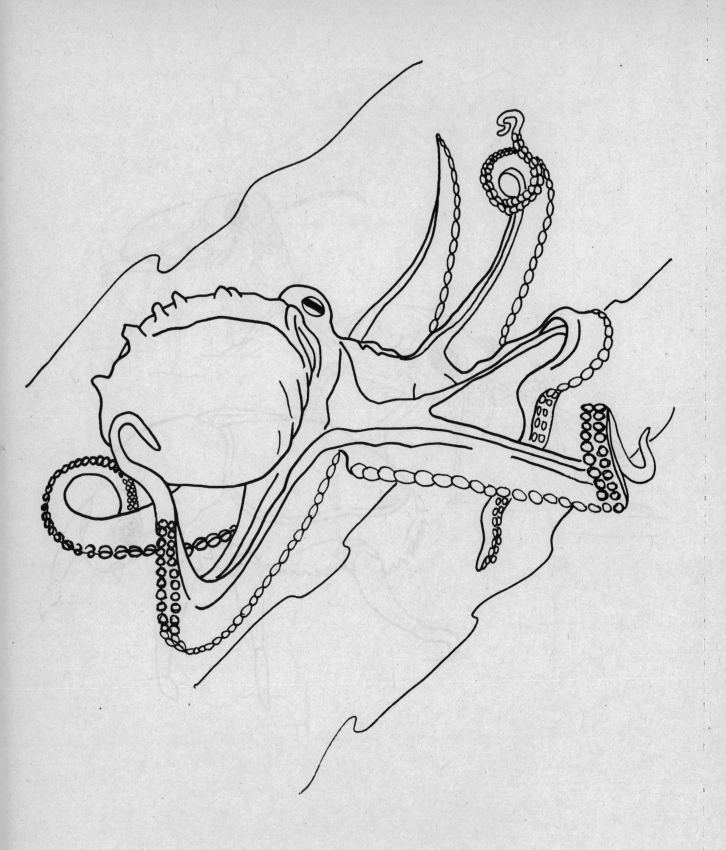

# There are 200 species of octopus in the world.

# Tiger

| 1=A | 8=H | 15=O | 22=V |
|-----|-----|------|------|
| 2=B | 9=I | 16=P | 23=W |
| 3=C | 10=J | 17=Q | 24=X |
| 4=D | 11=K | 18=R | 25=Y |
| 5=E | 12=L | 19=S | 26=Z |
| 6=F | 13=M | 20=T | |
| 7=G | 14=N | 21=U | |

$\overline{\phantom{xx}}$ $\overline{\phantom{xx}}$ $\overline{\phantom{xx}}$ $\overline{\phantom{xx}}$ $\overline{\phantom{xx}}$ $\overline{\phantom{xx}}$ $\overline{\phantom{xx}}$ $\overline{\phantom{xx}}$ $\overline{\phantom{xx}}$ $\overline{\phantom{xx}}$
18   8   9   14   15   3   5   18   15   19

**11.**

# COOL CODE

Using the code, write the letters on the line to find out which very large animal is a vegetarian!

See Answers

**It rains every day in the rainforest.**

**Turtle**

**The llama is the western camel's closest relative.**

**Male impala have
impressive lyre-shaped horns.**

**Deserts cover 1/3 of the Earth's surface.**

**Walruses live in large herds, often containing up to 2,000 individuals.**

# OCEAN ARCTIC JUNGLE

| O | D | F | R | T | Y |
|---|---|---|---|---|---|
| C | H | C | A | Z | P |
| E | L | G | N | U | J |
| A | K | H | F | T | Y |
| N | B | D | E | U | L |
| A | R | C | T | I | C |

**12.**

## HABITAT SEARCH

Find and circle some of the world's habitats found at the top of the page in the puzzle! Look up, down, across, and diagonally.

See Answers

**Zebras are a member of the horse family.**

# Bats

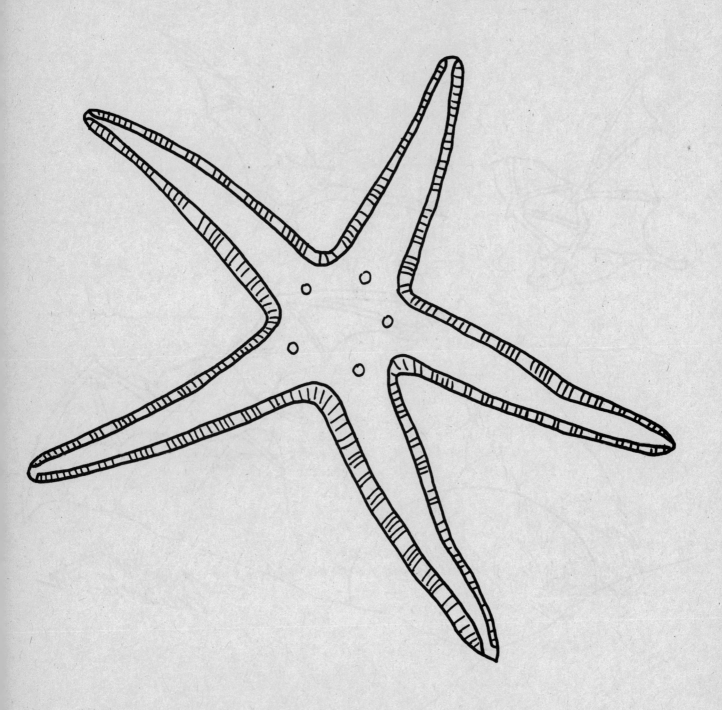

# Starfish can be found in rock pools and on beaches.

**Gorillas are the
largest of primates.**

# Mountains

**The largest coral reef is the Great Barrier Reef in Australia.**

**An elephant can suck up to 2 gallons of water into its trunk in one go!**

**The Arctic is the region around the North Pole.**

# A E T C H H E

\_\_\_\_ \_\_\_\_ \_\_\_\_ \_\_\_\_ \_\_\_\_ \_\_\_\_ \_\_\_\_

**13.**

## UNSCRAMBLE THE WORD

Unscramble the word to find out which animal can run the fastest!

See Answers

**A jaguar can be distinguished
from a leopard by its irregular spots
and shorter tail.**

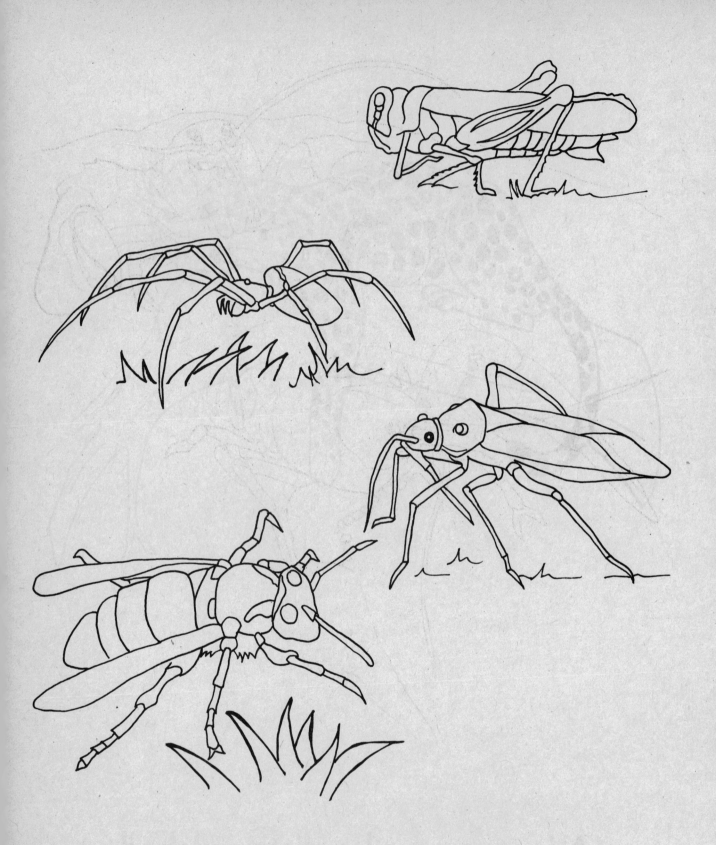

# Insects

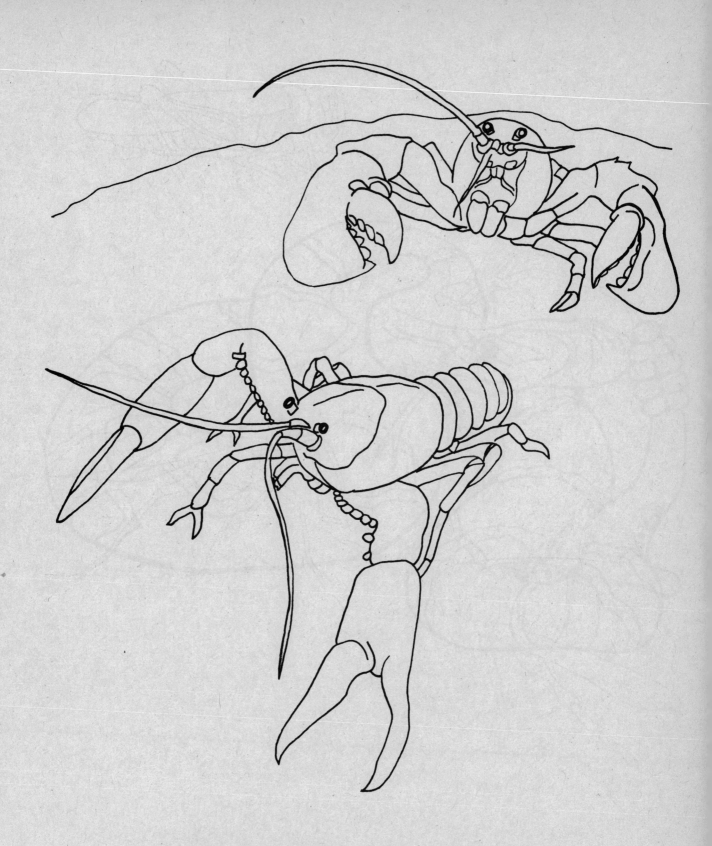

**Lobsters use the Earth's magnetic field as a compass.**

# Rattlesnake

# POLAR BEAR

_____          _____

_____          _____

_____          _____

_____          _____

**14.**

## HOW MANY WORDS?

How many three- and four-letter words can you make from the words NATURAL HABITAT? Write them on the lines.

See Answers

# Moose

**Wolf**

# ANSWERS

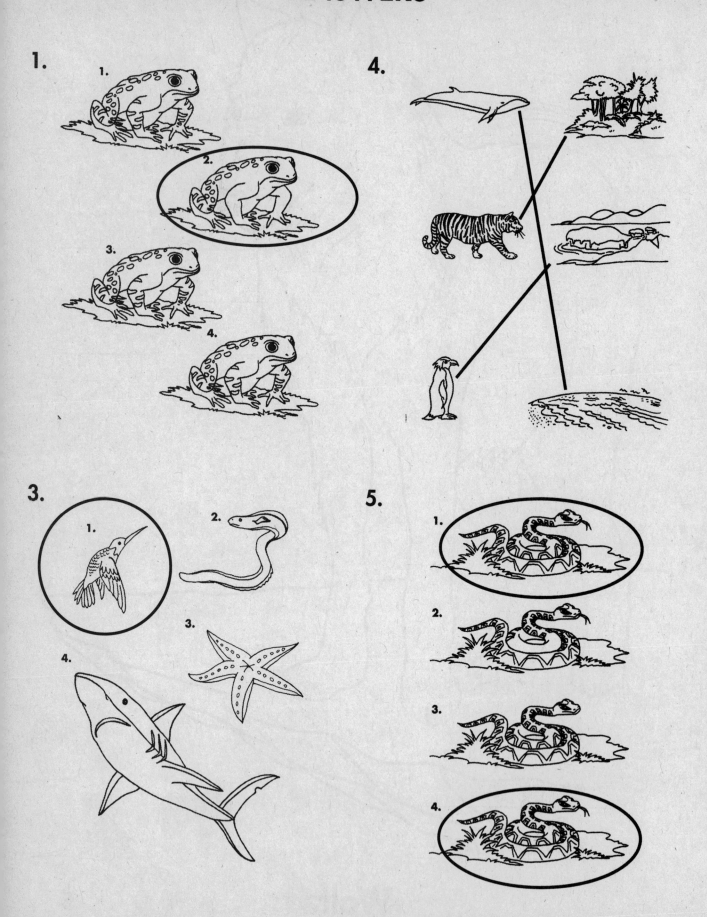

# ANSWERS

**6.**

**8.**

SOME POSSIBLE ANSWERS ARE:

**SLOTH**

**SNAIL**

**TURTLE**

**7.**

SOME POSSIBLE ANSWERS ARE:

**GRIZZLY BEAR**

**BLACK BEAR**

**KOALA BEAR**

**9.**

# ANSWERS

**10.**

### E A G L E

**SOME POSSIBLE ANSWERS ARE:**

| | |
|---|---|
| PEN | SAND |
| SAID | SEED |
| RAN | NEED |
| GEAR | SEE |

**11.**

### R H I N O C E R O S
18  8  9  14  15  3  5  18  15  19

**12.**

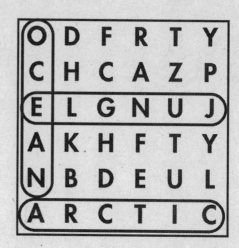

**13.**

### C H E E T A H

### P O L A R   B E A R

**14.**

**SOME POSSIBLE ANSWERS ARE:**

| | |
|---|---|
| HAT | RANT |
| TAN | RUN |
| BAIT | TAB |
| ANT | BAT |